THE PENGUIN'S™ PUT-DOWNS

JOKES AND RIDDLES

Scott Franklin & Batton Lash

TOR®

A TOM DOHERTY ASSOCIATES BOOK
NEW YORK

This is a work of fiction. All the characters and events portrayed in this book are fictitious, and any resemblance to real people or events is purely coincidental.

THE PENGUIN'S PUT-DOWNS, JOKES AND RIDDLES

Cover art by Howard Post
Interior art by Howard Post

A Tor Book
Published by Tom Doherty Associates, Inc.
175 Fifth Avenue
New York, N.Y. 10010

Tor ® is a registered trademark of Tom Doherty Associates, Inc.

ISBN: 0-812-52477-2

First printing: October 1992

Printed in the United States of America

0 9 8 7 6 5 4 3 2 1

What's black and white, black and white, and black and white?
The Penguin falling down the stairs!

What position does The Penguin take at a basketball game?
The fowl line!

What's black and white and black and blue?
The Penguin, after Batman gets through with him!

What does The Penguin take when he has the flu?
Penguin-cillin!

Why is The Penguin a good teacher?
He takes his students under his wing!

What two things does The Penguin never
eat for breakfast?
Lunch and dinner!

4

How does The Penguin fly?
When he boards a plane!

What kind of friend is The Penguin?
A fair-feathered one!

Why does The Penguin have so many
umbrellas?
He's saving them for a rainy day!

What is The Penguin's favorite salad?
Iceberg lettuce!

What did Batman do when The Penguin was
in the Bat-Cave?
Lined the floor with newspaper!

When is The Penguin not The Penguin?
When he turns chicken!

Why does Batman always out-smart The
Penguin?
The Penguin's a bird-brain!

What does The Penguin keep under his top
hat?
His head warm!

What do you call hair sticking out of
Batman's mask?
A cowl-lick!

How do you make The Penguin float?
*Put him in a bowl with two scoops of ice
cream!*

What animal does The Penguin refuse to
play cards with?
A cheetah!

What's worse than The Penguin robbing a bank?
The Penguin robbing your bank!

Why was fighting Batman like going to Hollywood!
Eventually, The Penguin was going to see stars!

What kind of pet does The Penguin have?
A bird dog!

Why was The Penguin always invited to dinner?
He ate like a bird!

Is The Penguin right-handed or left-handed?
Neither—he's underhanded!

What would you get if you crossed a
penguin and a skunk?
Something that stunk on ice!

Which one of The Penguin's crimes is the least dangerous?
A safe robbery!

Why did Batman hide the Batplane in his closet?
That's where he kept the hangar!

What crime did The Penguin accuse Batman of?
Assault and bat-tery!

What does Alfred make cookies with?
Bat-ter!

Why is The Penguin strong?
He can hold up banks!

How many penguins can fit in the Batmobile?
Six—two up front, two in the back and two in the glove compartment!

Why does The Penguin put on his right
shoe in the morning?
The wrong one would hurt his foot!

Why did Catwoman agree to be tied up by
The Penguin?
She was in ac-cord!

What's the first thing The Penguin does
after a good night's sleep?
Wakes up!

What is The Penguin's favorite fairy tale?
Cinderumbrella!

Why did Batman place a classified to
contact The Penguin?
He was on another ad-venture!

Why did Catwoman make fun of The
Penguin's weight?
*She liked to laugh at other people's
expanse!*

What kind of doctor did The Penguin go to?
A quack!

What kind of fight does Batman have with
The Penguin?
A fight to the fin-ish!

Why is The Penguin like a pastry?
They both can be dough-nuts!

How did The Penguin top Batman?
*By putting whipped cream and a cherry on
his head!*

What's black and white and turning blue?
The Penguin holding his breath!

What was wrong with The Penguin's
grammar when he was sent to jail?
He never finished a sentence!

Why was The Penguin like a carpenter?
They both took a hammer to attack!

Why did Bruce Wayne like the Bat-Cave?
It had a b-atmosphere!

What did Batman say when The Penguin tied and gagged him?
Mmmph!

How did The Penguin find the Bat-Cave?
He used the bat-roads that led to it!

What did The Penguin call the absent-minded carpenter?
A saw loser!

What happened when The Penguin crossed poison ivy and a four leaf clover?
He got a rash of good luck!

Why did the mermaid refuse to date The Penguin?
She was going out with the tide!

How do you spell Penguin backwards?
P-E-N-G-U-I-N B-A-C-K-W-A-R-D-S!

Why didn't Batman catch The Penguin in
the condominium?
The Penguin had already flown the co-op!

What was the first thing Batman learned in
school?
The alpha-bat!

What's black and white and yellow all over?
The Penguin hiding in a field of daisies!

What did The Penguin use to restrain the
mailman?
Chain letters!

What happened when The Penguin was caught stealing watches?
He did time!

What kind of bars did The Penguin want to see in jail?
Chocolate bars!

Why was Bruce Wayne so rich?
He had great interest in the banks!

Why didn't Batman see the glacier?
Poor ice-sight!

What did The Penguin use as a getaway from the North Pole?
An ice-cycle!

What happened when The Penguin tried to cross an octopus with a mink?
He got a fur coat with too many sleeves!

21

Why did The Penguin put firecrackers under his pancakes?
He felt like blowing his stack!

Why did The Penguin hold up the barber?
He wanted a cut of the action!

Why was The Penguin hiding under the bed?
If he was on top of it, he wouldn't be hiding!

What problems did Batman have with The Penguin and his dog?
One flees, the other has fleas!

What do The Penguin's umbrella and Alfred have in common?
They each get a raise now and then!

Why was the performer afraid of The Penguin?
He was afraid The Penguin would steal the spotlight!

What did The Penguin call the skeleton that wouldn't get out of bed?
Lazy bones!

Why did The Penguin steal the ornate painting?
He was going for baroque!

How did The Penguin make calls from prison?
He used a cell-ular phone!

Why was The Penguin in prison?
You guessed it—he was a cell-ebrity!

What's black and white and hides eggs?
The Easter Penguin!

What's black and white and is gone from 12–7?
The Penguin on his lunch break!

What fruit does The Penguin have after a
lobster dinner?
Crabapple!

Why was The Penguin born on the ground?
Penguins aren't airborne!

What's the difference between MC Hammer
and The Penguin?
*One has a rap beat while the other beats the
rap!*

What did the artist do when The Penguin
stole his painting?
He bristled!

What goes "wauk wauk ahhhchoo"?
The Penguin with an allergy!

What did The Penguin get when he crossed
a small fish and a Russian ruler?
A Czardine!

Why did The Penguin spray his hideout with insecticides?
He thought it was bugged!

Why did The Penguin wash his shirt at the stadium?
He wanted to use the bleachers!

What's black and white and is on the bottom of an elephant's back foot?
A slow-moving Penguin!

What's red and green and is on the bottom of an elephant's front foot?
An even slower moving Robin!

What was the name of the fort The Penguin hid in for two weeks?
Fort Nightly!

What did Batman say to the officer arresting a jurist who used The Penguin as an alibi?
"Don't book a judge by his cover!"

What's The Penguin's seafood diet?
He sees food and he eats it!

What's the difference between a courthouse
and The Penguin's freezer?
*One upholds justice, the other holds just
ice!*

What did The Penguin have in common
with the unemployed doctor?
No patience!

Who was the only person The Penguin was
afraid of at the baseball game?
The bat-boy!

Why did The Penguin smoke in his
hideout?
It was a bad habitat!

What did The Penguin get when he crossed
a parrot with a homing pigeon?
A bird that asks directions when it's lost!

What did The Penguin need to get into charm school?
Their savoir-fare!

What kind of bug goes along with The Penguin's schemes?
A particip-ant!

What happened when The Penguin met the kick-boxer?
They became arch-enemies!

What kind of vermin was a royal pain in the Wayne Manor?
Aristo-cats!

Why wasn't The Penguin afraid to steal the Venus Di Milo?
She was unarmed!

Why was The Penguin's prison cell mate
such a slow talker?
He spent ten years on a single sentence!

What happened when The Penguin asked
the oyster a personal question?
It clammed up!

What kind of gloves did The Penguin wear
for meetings with other bank robbers?
Sum-mitts!

Why did The Penguin never take a
vacation?
He was avoiding a rest (arrest)!

After a bank job, why did The Penguin put
his shoes in the freezer?
He was cooling his heels!

What did Bruce Wayne call Dick Grayson
when he was clumsy?
Awk-ward!

What did The Penguin say as he started to
touch his toes?
"This is the beginning of the bend!"

What did Batman find behind a vampire's house?
A bloodshed!

Why was The Penguin boasting he robbed a bank?
It was his brag to riches story!

Why was Bruce Wayne's party like The Penguin's career?
They both started out with capers!

Why did The Penguin have no regard for typesetters?
He knew they were involved with characters!

Why was The Penguin mad at his masseur?
He rubbed The Penguin the wrong way!

On a warm day, The Penguin caught 2 fish.
When he reached home, he had 3. How was
this possible?
He still had two fish—and one smelt!

Why did The Penguin rob a bank at the North Pole?
He wanted cold cash!

What happened when The Penguin asked an ice skater for a date?
She gave him the cold shoulder!

Why did The Penguin start counting when he was confused?
His daze was numbered!

What kind of tree does Batman hang his cape on to dry?
A cloak tree!

Why did The Penguin consider stealing a bushel of bananas?
It had plenty of appeal for him!

Why did The Penguin have a romantic reputation?
He was always flirting with the law!

What did The Penguin do when he saw the organ grinder?
He avoided the old crank!

Why was The Penguin sunburned?
He was always in The Gotham Sun!

Why did The Penguin leave his henchmen on the tiny island?
He had to get away from atoll!

Why does The Penguin give gum to panhandlers?
He says beggars can't be chewers!

Why did The Penguin gamble with Catwoman after midnight?
Bet her late than never!

What did Batman serve The Penguin at a party?
The punch!

What suit does The Penguin wear that he never irons, but wears in the bathtub?
His birthday suit!

Why did The Penguin rob the casino?
It was worth the gamble!

How does Commissioner Gordon contact Batman during a power failure?
He puts out the Bat-Shingle!

What did The Penguin win by default?
De election!

What would you call The Penguin if he was Batman's sidekick?
The Bird Wonder!

Why do the police suspect The Penguin
when he's holding an umbrella?
It makes The Penguin look shady!

Why did The Penguin eat a dollar bill?
He wanted to put his money where his mouth was!

There are many ways to commit crimes!
What's The Penguin Way?
Oh, about 288!

What does The Penguin go into to go out?
His bed!

What did the tailor do when The Penguin
broke into his shop?
Altered the press!

What did The Penguin say to the vermin
who stole his soap?
"You dirty rat!!!!"

Why did The Penguin break 500 pairs of
arms?
He wanted to see casts of thousands!

What did The Penguin's pet bird say when he refused to buy it treats?
"Cheep, cheep, cheep!"

Where does The Penguin carry his playing cards?
In his deck shoes!

What do Batman's favorite composer and The Penguin in jail have in common?
They're both Offenbach (off his back)!

Who is the cleanest super-hero in Gotham City?
Bathman!

What did The Penguin keep in an air-conditioned vault?
Cold cash!

How does The Penguin spell his name?
H-I-S N-A-M-E!

What's black and white and spins around?
The Penguin hiding in a washing machine!

Why did The Penguin push Batman down
the well?
He wanted him to kick the bucket!

What did The Penguin get when he crossed
a stream with a brook?
Wet feet!

What does The Penguin give to deaf fish?
A herring aid!

Why did The Penguin rob a bank with a
piece of lemon?
*He wanted to commit the crime with a little
twist!*

How is The Penguin affiliated with the
military?
Major Disasters follow him!

When won't The Penguin give The Joker
the time of day?
At night!

What spells *finis* for The Penguin?
A dictionary!

How did The Penguin stop waddling?
He sat down!

What's The Penguin's least favorite meal?
Eating crow!

Why did The Penguin want to work for a
coffee factory?
He heard about their perks!

Why did The Penguin bring a surfboard to rob banks?
He was riding a crime wave!

Why does The Penguin lock his kidnap victims in a dresser?
It's a missing persons bureau!

What happened when Batman and The Penguin gave each other gifts during a fire?
They had a heated exchange!

Why did The Penguin steal a diving board?
He decided to take the plunge!

What's The Penguin's idea of free speech?
Using someone else's phone!

Why are The Penguin's manners and a schoolhouse on Christmas the same?
They both have no class!

What kind of prison is The Penguin sent to?
A Penguin-tentiary!

Did you hear about The Penguin's card game?
It was no big deal!

Why doesn't The Penguin need a monocle in the Arctic?
His ice-sight gets better!

Why did The Penguin rob the fish market?
Just for the halibut!

What is The Penguin's favorite food?
A payroll!

Why didn't The Penguin know what to do when his last candle burned down?
He was at wick's end!

What did The Penguin say when he learned he weighed 288?
"I'm two gross!"

Why did The Penguin take a bath before breaking out of jail?
He wanted to make a clean getaway!

Why did The Penguin have to get on the scale in order to get an inheritance?
Where there's a will, there's a weigh!

What kind of paper did The Penguin make a kite with?
Fly paper!

Why did the judge give The Penguin ice cream and cookies in court?
He was serving him his just desserts!

When does The Penguin miss Batman?
When his aim is poor!

Why did The Penguin bring his umbrella to the castle?
He knew the King and Queen were reigning!

What did The Penguin call his ice sculpture?
A work of art-ic!

How can you tell that Catwoman's kitten loves thunderstorms?
When it rains, it purrs!

What city is dangerous to Catwoman?
Curios-city!

What kind of fish did The Penguin get a bargain on?
A sale-fish! (Sailfish.)

What bird can lift more weight than The Penguin?
A crane!

Why did The Penguin decide not to send a telegram to Washington?
Because he's dead!

What was wrong with The Penguin's complexion?
Whenever he was in jail, he'd break out!

What did The Penguin's umbrella say to his top hat?
"You go on ahead, I'll cover you!"

Why couldn't Batman go fishing?
Robin ate all the worms!

Why does The Penguin refuse to tell jokes while skating?
He's afraid the ice will crack up!

What is ABCDEFGHIJKLMNOPQRSTUVW XYZ slurrrp?
The sound of The Penguin eating alphabet soup!

What did The Penguin get when he crossed a movie house with a swimming pool?
A dive-in theatre!

Why does The Penguin tell little white lies?
Because he's am-fib-ious!

Why did The Penguin keep his word?
No one would take it!

Why didn't Catwoman want anyone to
operate on her boyfriend?
She didn't want anybody opening her male!

Why does The Penguin wear loud socks?
So his feet won't fall asleep!

What does The Penguin take off last before
he goes to bed?
He takes his feet off the floor!

What's wrong with The Penguin's grammar?
Nothing—she's a sweet old lady!

Why did The Penguin lose his job at the gym?
He just didn't work out!

Why does The Penguin find it so easy to weigh fish?
Because they have their own scales!

What do you call Catwoman when she wears make-up?
A glamour-puss!

What is Batman's favorite sport?
Bat-minton!

Why did Batman arrest the photographer?
For shooting people and blowing them up!

What's black and white and found in Florida?
A lost penguin!

Why was The Penguin saluting in the cornfield?
He saw kernels!

What did The Penguin call the frightened skin diver?
Chicken of the sea!

What did The Penguin call the cannibal who devoured his father's sister?
An aunt-eater!

Who is The Penguin's favorite actor?
Sean Penn-guin!

What's the difference between Catwoman and a comma?
Catwoman has claws at the end of her paws, a comma has a pause at the end of its clause!

Why is The Penguin afraid of the letter R?
It makes his beak break!

Why was The Penguin so tired in April?
He'd had a very long March!

How did The Penguin keep his fish from smelling?
He chopped off its nose!

When is the Catwoman not Catwoman?
When she turns into an alley!

What South American country is The Penguin most comfortable in?
Chile!

How did The Penguin eat breakfast without getting up?
He just took a few rolls in bed!

Why did The Penguin put a fish on his radio?
To give it more bass!

What suit has The Penguin never worn, but
wears him out?
A lawsuit!

Which part of The Penguin's clothing lasts the longest?
Underwear—it's never worn out!

What makes The Penguin happy when he plays chess?
Taking a knight off!

How can you tell if The Penguin has been in your refrigerator?
By the webbed footprints in the butter!

What do you get when you cross a penguin and a professor?
A formal education!

What did The Penguin get when he cleaned his stove with shaving cream?
Foam on the range!

What reaction did Catwoman get when she made jokes about The Penguin's stomach?
Belly laughs!

Why can't you believe The Penguin when he's in bed?
Because he's lying!

What does The Penguin do with the money he steals?
He puts it in his nest-egg!

What will go up a chimney "down" but won't go down a chimney "up"?
The Penguin's umbrella!

Why are The Penguin's birds poor?
Because they have so many bills!

Can The Penguin jump higher than the Empire State Building?
Of course—The Empire State Building can't jump!

What happened when The Penguin fell into the wet cement?
He became a hardened criminal!

Where does The Penguin keep his money?
In frozen assets!

What's the difference between Batman and The Penguin?
One has Robin, the other is robbin'!

Why is it better to be Catwoman than a frog?
Catwoman has nine lives, but a frog croaks all the time!

Why is The Penguin like a cub when he takes a bath?
Because he's a little bare!

What's the difference between a ballet dancer and a penguin?
One goes quick on her legs, and the other goes quack on her eggs!

What do you get when you cross a cow and a group of penguins?
Milk and quackers!

Why did The Penguin apply for the night watchman's job?
He wanted to make money without doing a day's work!

What's the difference between a storm cloud and The Penguin stubbing his toe?
One pours with rain and the other roars with pain!

What do penguins have that no other birds do?
Baby penguins!

What acting honor was Catwoman given?
The A-cat-emy Award!

Why did The Penguin rob a bakery?
Its cakes were rich!

How did the teapot feel when The Penguin stole it?
It was steamed!

What's the difference between a prizefighter and The Penguin with a cold?
One knows his blows and the other blows his nose!

Which of The Penguin's pet birds is the most religious?
The cardinal!

What's the difference between The Penguin when he's hungry and when he's being a glutton?
Sometimes he longs to eat and other times he eats too long!

Why won't Catwoman go bald like The Penguin?
She wears her hair longer!

Which bird is even madder than The Penguin?
A loon!

Why did the bank believe The Penguin when he said he wouldn't rob it?
It was a trust company!

What's the difference between The Penguin and a church bell?
One steals from the people and one peals from the steeple!

Why did The Penguin sit in the last row of the theatre to keep cool?
He wanted to be in the "z-row" seats!

What's the difference between a match and Catwoman?
A match lights on its head, but Catwoman lights on her feet!

Why are The Penguin's fish so intelligent?
They've spent so much time in schools!

Was The Penguin nervous when he hid
from Batman in the steam room?
He sweated out every minute!

What did The Penguin call the icicle?
An eaves-dropper!

What fish might you find in one of The Penguin's bird cages?
A perch!

In what country did The Penguin decide to go fishing?
Finland!

What's black and white and red all over?
An embarrassed penguin!

What do you call a penguin with straight "A"s on his report card?
A wise quacker!

How did the clock feel when The Penguin stole it?
Ticked off!

What did Batman say when The Penguin
escaped by crashing through a window?
"Well, that pane is gone!"

What did The Penguin get when he crossed a goose and a rhino?
An animal that honks before it runs you over!

What happened when The Penguin telephoned a bee?
He got a "buzzy" signal!

What color is Catwoman when she's happy?
Purr-ple!

What happened when The Penguin crossed a turkey and a centipede?
Everyone at Thanksgiving dinner got a drumstick!

Why did The Penguin pinch the waitress?
He wanted to see flying saucers!

What does The Penguin eat in the Arctic?
Chilly burgers!

What kind of bank did The Penguin see advertised on TV?
A commercial bank!

How many penguins does it take to change a light bulb?
One—but he can't reach!

Why did The Penguin hire Robinson Crusoe's servant?
He wanted all of his work done by Friday!

How did The Penguin pass the geometry test?
He knew all the angles!

What did the herring say to The Penguin?
"Am I my brother's kipper?"

Why did The Penguin cross the street?
To get over the state line!

How did The Penguin keep his food bills down?
He used a heavier paperweight!

How did The Penguin inspire The Joker?
The Joker let the umbrella be his smile!

What did The Penguin say when he was saved from the hangman?
"No noose is good news!"

How did The Penguin begin his book on waterfowl?
With an intro-duck-tion!

What song did The Penguin sing to his octopus?
I want to hold your hand, hand, hand, hand, hand, hand, hand, hand!

What's stranger than seeing The Penguin play tennis?
Seeing a goldfish bowl!

What happened when The Penguin
accidentally swallowed a doorknob?
His stomach kept turning!

What did The Penguin eat that stunted his
growth?
Shortening bread!

How did The Penguin mend his broken
heart?
With ticker tape!

Where does Catwoman vacation in the
winter?
Meow-mi Beach!

What did The Penguin get when he was
caught in the rain on Friday?
Saturday Night Fever!

What did The Penguin give to the canary
with the broken leg?
First-aid tweetment!

What does The Penguin raise during the
rainy season?
His umbrella!

What's black and white and hides in caves?
A penguin that owes money!

What did The Penguin get when he stuck
his nose in a socket?
An electric bill!

Why doesn't The Penguin trust fishermen
and shepherds?
Because they live by hook and by crook!

What did The Penguin call the scared flower arranger?
A petrified florist!

How did Batman help find the missing barber?
By combing the city!

What did The Penguin get when he crossed his parrot and his woodpecker?
A bird that talks in Morse code!

What two garden vegetables fight crime?
Beetman and Radish!

Why did The Penguin apply for a job in the mint?
He heard workers could make a million dollars in a day!

How would you make Catwoman fly?
Buy her an airline ticket!

What did The Penguin call the sunburn on his belly?
Pot roast!

Why didn't The Penguin get hurt when he leapt off a building?
He was wearing his light fall suit!

What is the sharpest part of Catwoman's body?
Her shoulder blades!

When does a cold get the best of The Penguin?
When it brings him to his sneeze!

Who delivers mail to Catwoman?
A litter carrier!

What would you get if you crossed Catwoman with an octopus?
I don't know what you'd call it, but it would have eight arms and nine lives!

What kind of diploma does The Penguin usually get?
The third degree!

Why did The Penguin take a job as a store detective?
He always wanted to be a counter spy!

Why does The Penguin keep getting smarter?
Because the judges keep throwing the book at him!

Why did The Penguin put his father in the freezer?
He wanted to make a pop-sicle!

How is a sinking ship like The Penguin in jail?
They both need bailing out!

What's The Penguin's idea of a cold war?
A snowball fight!

Why does Batman brush his teeth three times a day?
To prevent bat breath!

When is it socially acceptable to serve milk in a saucer?
When you're serving Catwoman!

Why won't Batman get married?
He wants to remain a bat-chelor!

Why did The Penguin eat lots of chocolate bars in prison?
He was hoping he could break out!

What can overpower Batman without hurting him?
Sleep!

Why didn't The Penguin enjoy his trip to the aquarium?
He didn't see the porpoise in it!

Why did The Penguin cut a hole in the top of his umbrella?
To see when it would stop raining!

Which pet is the most valuable in The
Penguin's menagerie?
His gold fish!

What was Batman's name when he fought
The Penguin?
Bruised Wayne!

How did The Penguin catch an electric eel?
With a lightning rod!

How can The Penguin do without sleep for
7 days and still not be tired?
He sleeps at night!

Why did The Penguin cross the street
twice?
He's a double crosser!

What did The Penguin find the hardest part
of ice skating?
The ice!

What did The Penguin get when he crossed
an owl and a goat?
A hootenanny!

If The Penguin smashed a clock, could he be accused of killing time?
Not if the clock struck first!

What fish do penguins eat?
Anything that fits the bill!

What is Catwoman's favorite dessert?
Mice pudding!

What fish does The Penguin love to eat with peanut butter?
Jellyfish!

What did The Penguin get when he crossed an octopus and a cow?
An animal that could milk itself!

What is the hardest thing for The Penguin
to keep in hot weather?
Cool!

What did The Penguin's insurance company
pay him for a bump on the head?
A lump sum!

What two super heroes were run down by a
steamroller?
Flatman and Ribbon!

Why did Catwoman call her new kitten
"Peeve"?
Because everyone has a pet peeve!

The Penguin and six of his henchmen stood under his umbrella. How come none of them got wet?

It wasn't raining!

How did The Penguin spell "slippery" in
just two letters?
"I.C.!"

What happened when The Penguin threw a red stone into the Black Sea?
It got wet!

How did The Penguin make the baby snake cry?
He took away its rattle!

Why did Batman think he could save money by trading the Batmobile for a boat?
Because boats run on water!

Where did The Penguin go to see a man-eating fish?
A seafood restaurant!

Why did The Penguin weep whenever he got into a fight?
It was his battle-cry!

Why did The Penguin take a calendar on his
trip to the desert?
*So he could eat the dates and drink the
water from the spring!*

Why does The Penguin dislike traffic cops?
They always make him cross!

Why did Batman and The Penguin fly to
Scandinavia?
*They were going to have a flight to the
Finnish!*

Why did The Penguin wear a tuxedo when
he had his appendix removed?
*He wanted to dress formally for the
opening!*

What did The Penguin get when he crossed
a parrot and a shark?
An animal that talks your ear off!

Which of The Penguin's pet birds is most
worried about hygiene?
*His rooster—he never lends anyone his
comb!*

What teeth did The Penguin buy for a dollar?
Buck teeth!

What did The Penguin get when he crossed a raccoon and a skunk?
A dirty look from the raccoon!

What's the difference between the rear of the Batmobile and a book of short stories?
One has tail lights, the other has light tales!

What did the new bride and groom hold in The Penguin's hideout?
A chilly reception!

Why did The Penguin easily defeat the tuna in a tennis match?
The tuna was afraid to get close to the net!

Where did The Penguin keep his money?
In a snow bank!

What object of The Penguin's is most useful when it's used up?
His umbrella!

Why did The Penguin refuse to believe what his doctor said?
He kept making M.D. promises!

What's black and white, turns green and burps?
The Penguin after too many hot dogs!

Why does The Penguin need to bathe a lot?
Because he's a dirty crook!

How much birdseed did The Penguin buy for a quarter?
None—quarters don't eat birdseed!

What do penguins get under their eyes when they can't sleep?
Arctic circles!

Why did The Penguin break out of jail?
It was making him cagey!

What kind of reception did The Penguin get at the Ice Capades?
A frosty one!

What did Batman say when The Penguin came after him with a fishing rod?
"Don't give me that line!"

What's black and white, black and white, and flickers?
The Penguin watching an old movie!

What's the hippest piece of furniture in The Penguin's house?
The rocking chair!

Why did The Penguin take hay to bed with him?
To feed his night-mares!

Where does The Penguin keep his loose change?
His chair—that's where he puts his hind quarters!

Where did The Penguin go for a sandwich in India?
New Delhi!

Why did Batman hate following The Penguin to the Arctic?
It just left him cold!

When The Penguin's jacket got too tight, why wouldn't he diet?
He liked the color it already was!

What happened when Catwoman ate a lemon?
She became a sour puss!

What kind of birds does The Penguin hate?
Stool pigeons!

How did The Penguin cure his acid
indigestion?
He stopped drinking acid!

Why did Catwoman scratch a hole in the floor?
She wanted to see the floor show!

Why is Catwoman at the beach like Christmas?
Because of the sandy claws!

Which of The Penguin's pet birds is the rudest?
The mocking bird!

Who performed surgery on The Penguin's pet fish?
The head sturgeon!

What did The Penguin get when he stuck his nose in a socket?
An electric bill!

Why did The Penguin apply for a
fisherman's job?
He heard about the net profits!

What musical instrument helps The
Penguin fish?
Cast-a-net!

Why is Catwoman usually well-rested?
She takes plenty of cat-naps!

What happened when The Penguin slipped
on thin ice?
His backside was thaw!

Where does Catwoman keep her money?
In a kitty!

Why was The Penguin like two people when he got angry?
He was beside himself!

Why is The Penguin such a big eater?
Because he takes a peck at a time!

Why does Catwoman tell the same stories
over and over?
She's just a cat o' nine tales!

What do penguins hope to win in a lottery?
A cool million!

What happened when The Penguin tried to
become a psychic?
He went from bad to medium!

What vegetable did The Penguin raise in his
hideout?
Chilly peppers!

How did The Penguin make antifreeze?
He locked her in his hideout!

What's the difference between Catwoman and a mouse?
One charms the "he's" and the other harms the cheese!

Where do penguins go to dance?
A snow ball!

If you pull it, it's a cane; if you push it, it's a tent. What is it?
The Penguin's umbrella!

What is The Penguin's dieting motto?
If at first you don't recede, try, try again!

Why did The Penguin do so well in the fish selling business?
He started out on a small scale!

What's the difference between a lazy
student and The Penguin when he's
fishing?
*One hates his books and the other baits his
hook!*

Why was The Penguin's calendar
frightened?
Because its days were numbered!